It's another Quality Book from CGP

This book has been carefully written for Year 6 children learning science. It's full of questions and investigations designed to cover the Year 6 objectives on 'Animals, including humans' from the latest National Curriculum.

There's also plenty of practice at 'Working Scientifically' throughout the book.

What CGP is all about

Our sole aim here at CGP is to produce the highest quality books — carefully written, immaculately presented and dangerously close to being funny.

Then we work our socks off to get them out to you — at the cheapest possible prices.

Contents

Answers to the questions are on the back of the Pull-out Poster in the centre of the book.

Published by CGP

Contributors
Christopher Lindle, Sarah Pattison, Sean Stayte
With thanks to Katie Braid and Amanda MacNaughton for the proofreading.

ISBN: 978 1 78294 092 0

Clipart from Corel®
Printed by Elanders Ltd, Newcastle upon Tyne.
Based on the classic CGP style created by Richard Parsons.

The Human Body

You probably know your body quite well — after all, you've used it every day since you were born. This page will test how well you know all the stuff that's <u>inside</u> your body, keeping you alive...

1. Have a look at the three bodies below and write down what each one is showing. Choose from **muscles**, **digestive system**, or **skeleton**.

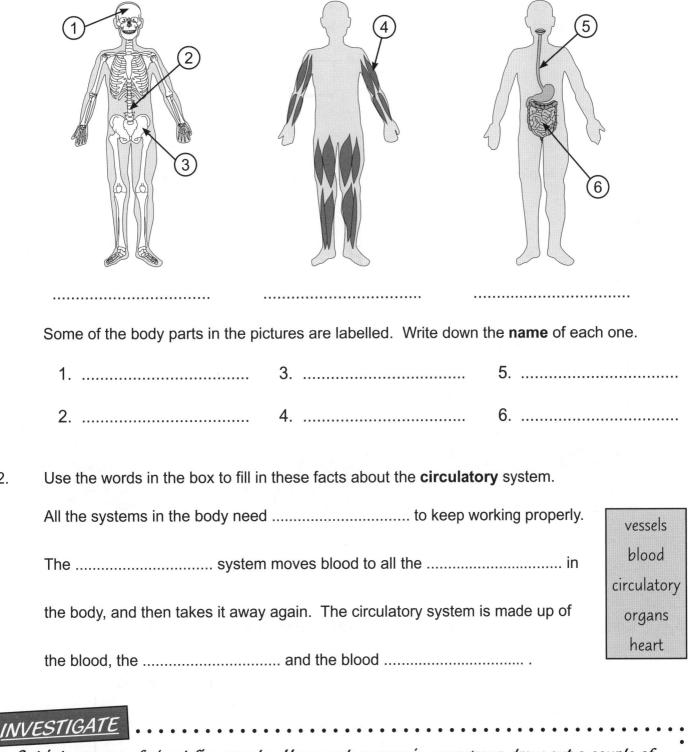

....

Some of the body parts in the pictures are labelled. Write down the **name** of each one.

1. .... 3. .... 5. ....

2. .... 4. .... 6. ....

2. Use the words in the box to fill in these facts about the **circulatory** system.

All the systems in the body need .... to keep working properly.

The .... system moves blood to all the .... in

the body, and then takes it away again. The circulatory system is made up of

the blood, the .... and the blood ....

| vessels |
| blood |
| circulatory |
| organs |
| heart |

- *Get into groups of about five people. Have each person in your group draw out a couple of different organs of the body and colour them in. Use a really big piece of paper to draw the outline of a body, then take turns to put your organs in the right place on the outline.*

The Heart

Your <u>heart</u> is pretty important — it has to keep <u>beating</u> all the time to keep you alive.
Every time it beats, the heart pumps <u>blood</u> around your body.

1.   Put a tick (✔) next to the correct **location** of the heart in the body.

The heart is
inside the skull. ☐

The heart is
inside the ribcage. ☐

The heart is
in the legs. ☐

The heart is in
the stomach. ☐

2.   Here are **five** pictures of a heart. Circle the heart which is the right **size** and **shape**.

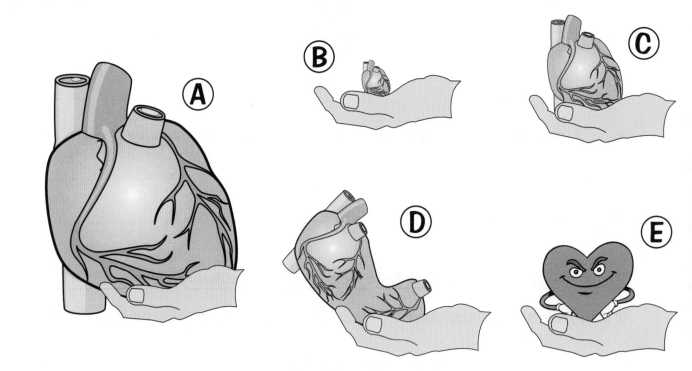

3.   Complete the sentence using the right words from the brackets.

The ribcage forms a hard wall of .... (**bones** / **blood**)

to .... (**soften** / **protect**) the heart and lungs.

The Heart

4. Use **some** of the words in the heart below to fill in the gaps in these sentences.

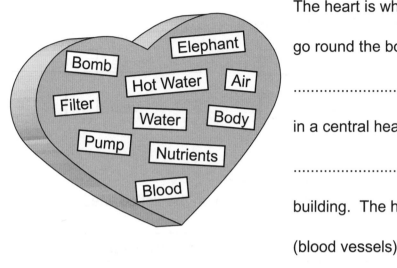

The heart is what makes ....

go round the body. The heart works as a

.... It's a bit like a water pump

in a central heating system; the pump pushes

.... through all the radiators in a

building. The heart pushes blood through tubes

(blood vessels) to the whole ....

The blood contains .... and .... needed by the body.

5. Complete these sentences by putting a (circle) around the correct words in the brackets.

The (**organs** / **walls**) of the heart are made of

(**muscle** / **bone**). It is called a (**dilation** / **contraction**)

when the muscles (**squeeze** / **attack**) blood out of the heart.

Describe how the heart pushes blood around the body when it beats.

....

....

....

INVESTIGATE ●

Write down some different-sized animals. Then use the Internet to find out how big their hearts are. Can you find an animal which has a smaller heart than a human? What about one which has a bigger heart? Which animal has the biggest heart of all?

4

Blood and Blood Vessels

The heart is just one part of the <u>circulatory system</u>. Every time your heart beats, <u>blood</u> is pushed to every part of your body through a series of tubes called <u>blood vessels</u>.

1. Put a tick next (✔) to the **three** kinds of blood vessel.

    Capillary ☐   Bone ☐   Nerve ☐

    Artery ☐   Muscle ☐   Vein ☐

2. These three sentences about blood vessels are **wrong**.
    Correct the **bold** words and write the new sentences out on the dotted lines.

    > Arteries carry blood away from the **body** and to the **heart**.

    > Blood is carried away from the body back to the heart by **muscles**.

    > Capillaries allow substances to move in and out of the **heart**.

    Arteries ....

    Blood ....

    Capillaries ....

3. (Circle) **four** things that are **transported** around the body in the blood.

    bits of plastic   water   carbon dioxide   nutrients

    badgers   blood vessels   oxygen   thoughts

    The blood **transports** waste products around the body.
    Which of the things listed above is a **waste product** that the body makes?

    ....

    The blood transports **oxygen** to all parts of the body.
    Where in the body does the blood **pick up** oxygen?

    ....

4

Blood and Blood Vessels

4. Here's a diagram of the heart and some of the main blood vessels in the body.
    Draw in the **arteries, veins, muscles** and **bits of brain** that are missing.

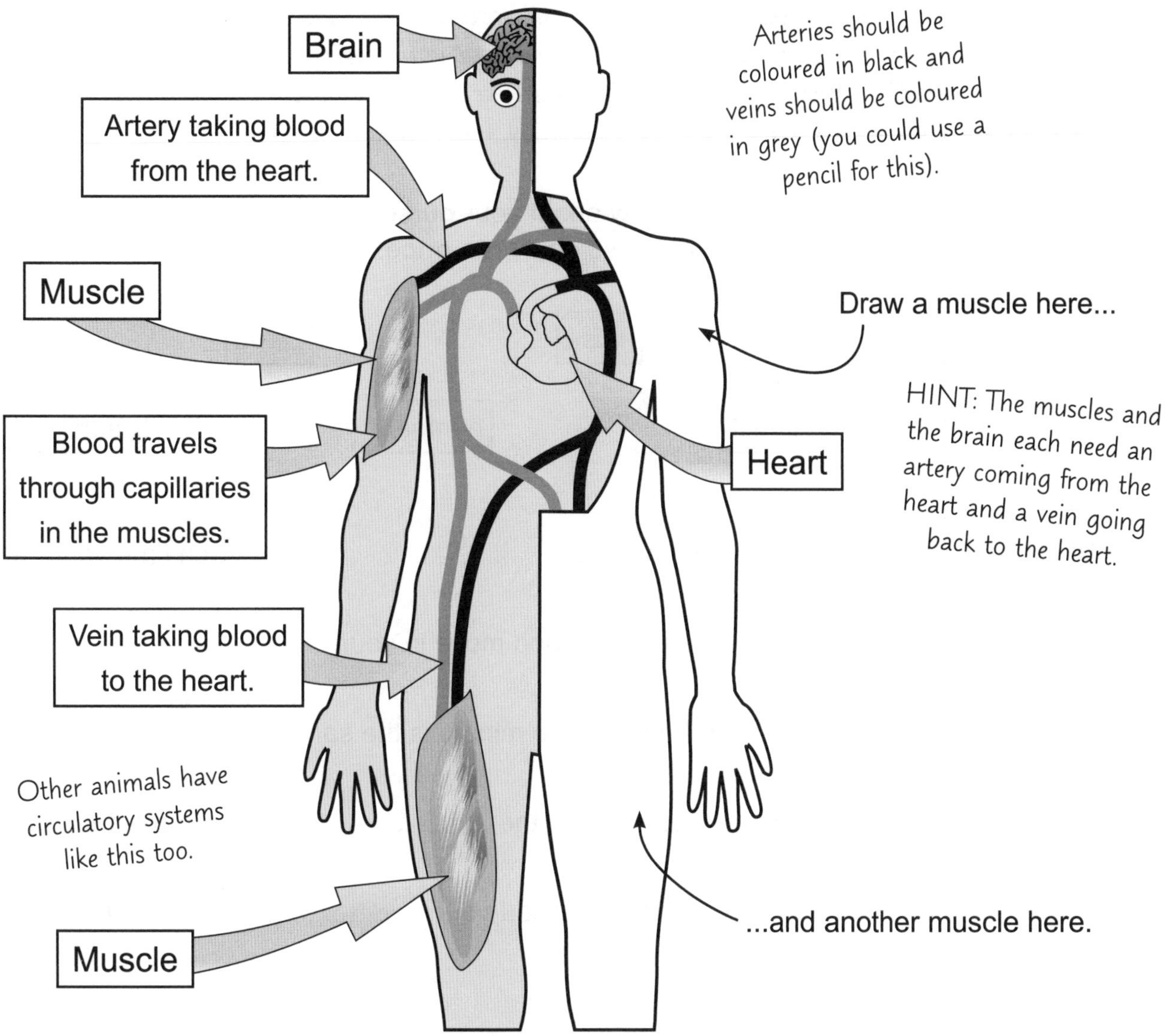

Brain

Artery taking blood
from the heart.

Muscle

Blood travels
through capillaries
in the muscles.

Vein taking blood
to the heart.

Other animals have
circulatory systems
like this too.

Muscle

Arteries should be
coloured in black and
veins should be coloured
in grey (you could use a
pencil for this).

Draw a muscle here...

Heart

HINT: The muscles and
the brain each need an
artery coming from the
heart and a vein going
back to the heart.

...and another muscle here.

5. Describe the journey of blood from the heart to a muscle, and back to the
    heart again. Mention **arteries**, **veins** and **capillaries** in your answer.

You can use the
diagram above to
help you answer
this question.

....

....

....

....

INVESTIGATE . . . .

- Create a poster that shows everything you know about the heart and blood vessels.
- Make sure you explain how the heart works and how blood travels around your body.

Section 1 — The Circulatory System

6

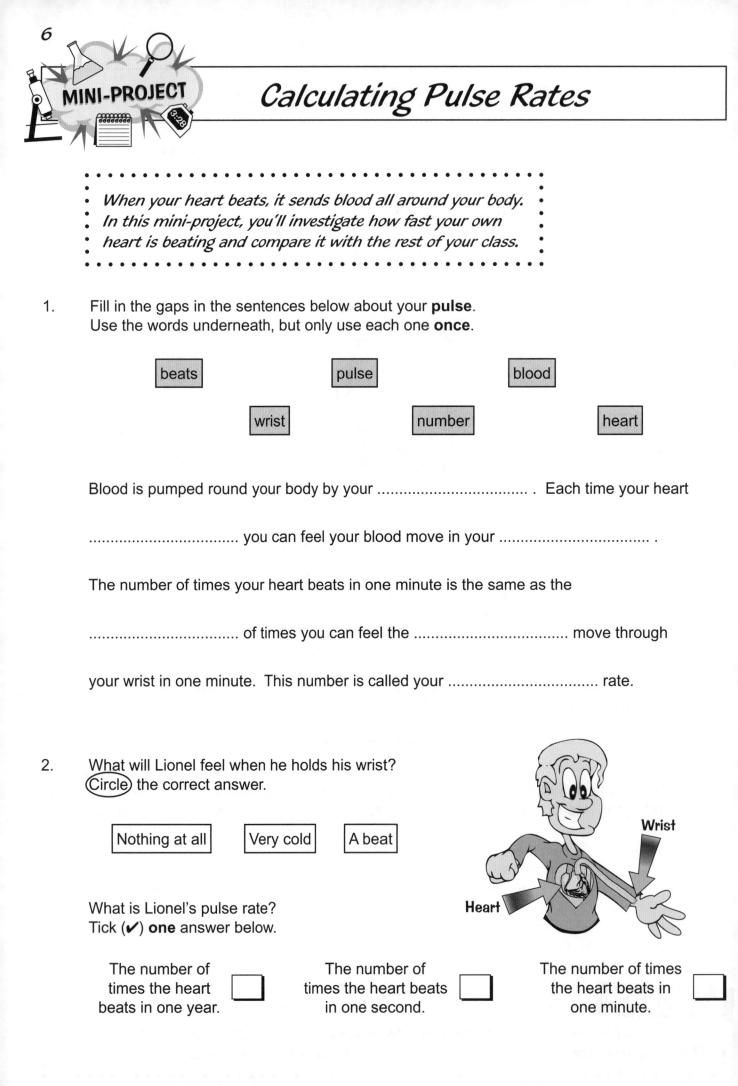

Calculating Pulse Rates

When your heart beats, it sends blood all around your body. In this mini-project, you'll investigate how fast your own heart is beating and compare it with the rest of your class.

1. Fill in the gaps in the sentences below about your **pulse**. Use the words underneath, but only use each one **once**.

beats   pulse   blood

wrist   number   heart

Blood is pumped round your body by your .... Each time your heart

.... you can feel your blood move in your ....

The number of times your heart beats in one minute is the same as the

.... of times you can feel the .... move through

your wrist in one minute. This number is called your .... rate.

2. What will Lionel feel when he holds his wrist? Circle the correct answer.

Nothing at all   Very cold   A beat

What is Lionel's pulse rate?
Tick (✔) **one** answer below.

The number of times the heart beats in one year. ☐

The number of times the heart beats in one second. ☐

The number of times the heart beats in one minute. ☐

Calculating Pulse Rates

MINI-PROJECT

3.   Count the number of beats you can feel on the inside of your wrist in 30 seconds.
     Do this **five** times and write your results in the table below.

Sit still for two minutes before starting
to take measurements. This means you'll
be measuring your <u>resting pulse rate</u>.

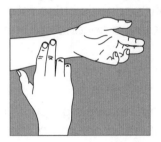

Beats in 30 seconds

Take your pulse by gently pressing your fingers on the
inside of your left wrist and counting the beats of blood
you can feel. (If you can't feel anything you might need
to move your fingers around or press harder.)

4.   Was the result the same each time? Write **yes** or **no**.

....

5.   If your result **wasn't** the same each time, why do you think this was?
     Circle any of the reasons below that you think are true.

You might have missed a beat,
so you counted incorrectly.

Your heart beat never ever changes.

Your pulse rate may go up and down a
little bit even if you're just sitting still.

You always count wrong at least once.

Sometimes your blood flows backwards.

Section 1 — The Circulatory System

Calculating Pulse Rates

6. Get into pairs and take your **partner's pulse** using the instructions and table below.

Beats in 30 seconds	Pulse rate (beats per minute)

1. Count the beats in your partner's left wrist for 30 seconds and write it in the first column.

2. Then multiply the result by 2 to get your partner's pulse rate. Write it in the second column.

You multiply by 2 because there are 60 (2 x 30) seconds in a minute.

3. Do this three times.

Now you can use your measurements to work out an **average** pulse rate.
First **add** together the pulse rates from the **right-hand** column of the table above.

....

Divide that number by 3 to get your partner's **average** pulse rate.
Give your answer to the nearest whole number.

....

Now get your partner to work out your average pulse rate using the same method.

7. Collect all your **class results** together in this tally chart.
If you can't collect other people's results use the spare results at the bottom of the page.

Here's how to use the chart...

A pulse rate of 92 fits into the 90 – 94 group. So for this result you'd put a tally mark in this row.

Average Pulse Rate (beats per minute)	Tally	Frequency
69 and below		
70 – 74		
75 – 79		
80 – 84		
85 – 89		
90 – 94		
95 – 99		
100 – 104		
105 and above		

Once you've filled in all the class results, add up the tally marks for each group and write the total in the frequency column.

Spare Results: 75, 96, 100, 83, 82, 87, 94, 96, 91, 92, 93, 101, 95, 93, 91, 99, 98, 77, 105, 108, 102, 97, 86, 73, 94, 90, 89

Calculating Pulse Rates

MINI-PROJECT

8. Use the results from the tally table on the last page to fill in this **bar chart**.
Each pulse rate group (like 85 – 89 for example) is called a **pulse rate range**.
Make each bar a different colour.

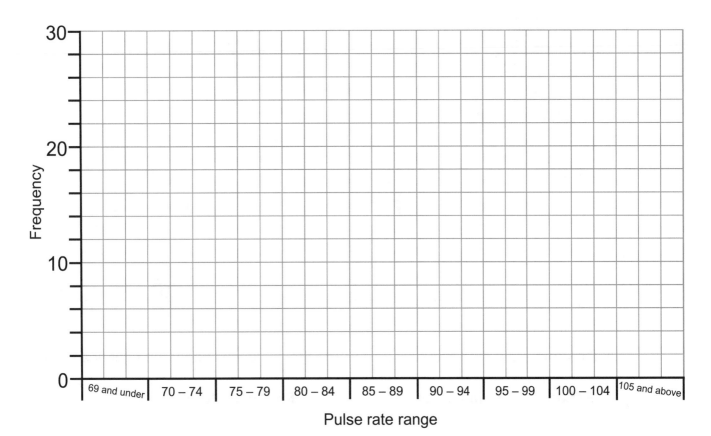

9. Use your **bar chart** to answer the questions below.

Which was the **most** common pulse rate range?

....

Which was the **second most** common pulse rate range?

....

Which was the **least** common pulse rate range?

....

EXTRA PROJECT

Find the average pulse rate of five adults. Compare the result to the results for your class. Do the adults have a higher or lower average pulse rate than the most common pulse rate range for your class? Why do you think this is?

Section 1 — The Circulatory System

Section 2 — Keeping Healthy

A Balanced Diet

Eating the right food is really important if you want to be healthy, grow loads and do lots of active stuff. What you've got to do is have a healthy <u>balanced diet</u>.

1. Here are **four** people having their dinner. (Circle) the ones who are eating a balanced diet.

Susan

Patrick

Lena

Eoin

2. Fill in the **table** using the sentences below. Put the sentences under the right headings.

Eating well should mean you will...	Eating badly could mean you will...

★ Grow well.

★ Get fat.

★ Be able to do lots of sport.

★ Have loads of energy.

★ Have to have loads of fillings in your teeth.

★ Get tired a lot.

★ Not feel so good.

★ Have strong bones and muscles.

INVESTIGATE ....

What kinds of food do you think you need for a balanced diet? Look at the pictures in question 1 — for each person who is not eating a balanced diet, write down why you think their dinner isn't healthy and make a list of some foods that they could eat instead.

Types of Food

Food can be put into different <u>groups</u> — like fish, meat, vegetables, fruit and fats. You've got to know about these groups because they're a big part of what makes you strong and healthy.

1. Here are some pictures of different kinds of food — write which group they belong to in the space below them. The groups are in the box on the right.

sausages

....

pear

....

fish

vegetables

meat

fruit

fats

cabbage

....

butter

....

salmon

....

steak

....

carrots

....

olive oil

sardines

....

....

banana

....

INVESTIGATE ....

Make a list of some foods in your cupboards at home. For each one, work out which group of food it belongs to. Can you find any foods that don't fit into the groups on this page?

© CGP — not to be photocopied   Section 2 — Keeping Healthy

Foods for Energy and Foods for Growth

Some kinds of food are especially important for helping you to <u>grow</u>.
Other foods give you <u>energy</u>, so you can do loads of running about without feeling really tired.

1. Some of the foods below are good sources of **energy**, and others are great for helping you **grow**.
    Write the name of each food in the correct box in the table to show what it is most useful for.

 rice

beef

fish

milk

spaghetti

chips

Good for Energy	Good for Growth

2. Catrina is running a marathon, so she's eaten lots of food that will give her energy.
    Order these sentences **1-5** to describe how the food gets from her mouth to her muscles.
    The first one has been done for you.

☐ The blood takes the nutrients back to the heart.

☐ The heart beats and sends the blood with the nutrients to her muscles.

☐ The food gets broken down as it goes through her digestive system.

☐ When it gets to the small intestine, the nutrients are absorbed into the blood.

1 She chews and swallows the food.

INVESTIGATE •
Write down a list of all the food you've eaten today. From the list, identify which foods are
for growth and which are for energy. Ask an adult to help look up foods you're not sure of.

Sugar and Fat

Sugar and fat are fine if you only eat a small amount of them, but it's a really
bad idea to eat <u>too much</u> — although sometimes it's hard to resist...

1. For each of the foods below, decide whether each one contains **loads of sugar**, **loads of fat**
   or **both**. Write **sugar**, **fat** or **both** below each food. There are two foods that contain both.

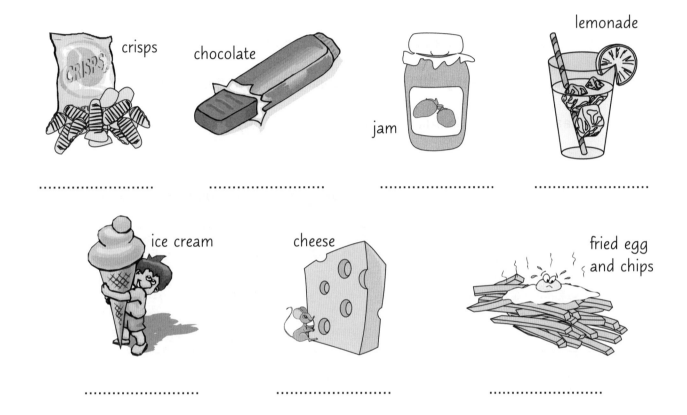

crisps   chocolate   jam   lemonade

....

ice cream   cheese   fried egg and chips

....

2. Fill in the gaps in these sentences using the **words** in the blob on the right.

If you eat lots of fatty foods, you might get ....

Eating too much sugar is bad for your ....

and might mean you have to have ....

If you eat too much sugar and fat instead of other foods,

like .... , your diet won't be balanced and

that means you won't be so ....

TEETH

FAT

VEGETABLES

HEALTHY

FILLINGS

INVESTIGATE ·

Make a poster about healthy eating and the problems caused by eating too many sugary
and fatty foods. Include some examples of foods that people shouldn't eat too often.

Section 2 — Keeping Healthy

Fruit and Vegetables

I know you may not want to hear this, but fruit and vegetables are <u>mega important</u>.
Eat enough fruit and veg, and you'll be healthier and less likely to get ill. Sounds good to me...

1. Complete these sentences by putting a (circle) around the correct word in the brackets.

   Fruit and vegetables have loads of (**fibre** / **fat**) in them. You also get most of

   your (**sugar** / **vitamins**) from fruit and vegetables. Vitamins are useful for

   keeping you (**healthy** / **ill**) and for stopping you from getting (**old** / **ill**). You get

   (**meat** / **minerals**) in fruit and vegetables too. They help to keep you healthy.

2. Draw a **healthy meal** on each of these plates by choosing foods from the list below.

fish fingers	beans	sausages	strawberries	potatoes	eggs
tomato sauce	orange juice	biscuits	bread	rice	carrots
chicken	milk	banana	honey	cheesecake	salad

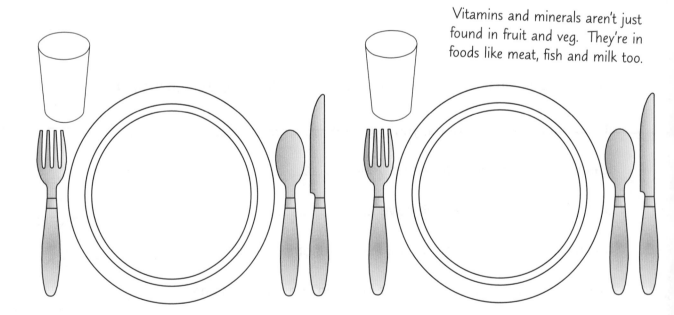

Vitamins and minerals aren't just found in fruit and veg. They're in foods like meat, fish and milk too.

INVESTIGATE ....

How many fruit and vegetables do you think you eat per day? Write down all the fruit and veg that you eat each day for a week. Did you eat more or less than what you thought?

Answers to Y6 'Circulation & Keeping Healthy'

Page 14 — Fruit and Vegetables

1. fibre, vitamins, healthy, ill, minerals
2. The meals drawn on the plates should show a healthy mix of the different types of food. Good examples include:
   chicken, beans, rice, orange juice
   fish fingers, salad, bread, carrots and milk
   banana, salad, milk, eggs, beans

Page 15 — Testing an Idea

1. E.g. It did help to make it a fair test. If he had changed more than one thing he wouldn't have known which change made the men better.
2. E.g. He chose patients that all had similar symptoms. / All the patients were in the same cabin.
3. Do the same test again with 12 other sick sailors.

Pages 16-17 — Exercise

1. Carl, Holly, Tony, Maddie, The Johnson Brothers, Theo
2. Pierre, Raj, Frederick
3-5. Depends on your results.
   Here's the table for my results:

	Number of breaths taken per minute
When relaxed	12
After exercise	28
3 minutes after exercise	16

6. E.g. After exercise I was taking more breaths per minute than when I was relaxed.
7. E.g. no
8. good, harder, strong, less healthy

Pages 18-19 — Exercise and Your Pulse

1. exercise, energy, beat, pulse
2. E.g. Playing table tennis mostly uses arm muscles, so Chad's arms will need more energy when he is playing table tennis. Swimming mostly uses arm and leg muscles, so Yao's arms and legs will need more energy when he is swimming. Running mostly uses leg muscles, so Lori's legs will need more energy when she is running.
3. running   4. 2000 m
5. Hurdling, Hiking for 50 minutes, Swimming quickly for 65 metres, Cycling.

Pages 20-22 — How Exercise Affects Pulse Rate

1. 4 - 10 people
2. The exercise used should be circled.
3. Depends on your results.
   Here's the table for the spare results.

Name:	Me	Ed	Liz	Jo	Average
Normal pulse rate	72	80	78	90	80
Pulse rate after half a minute of exercise	94	99	97	110	100
Pulse rate after 1 minute of exercise	135	125	133	127	130
Pulse rate after 1 and a half minutes of exercise	152	146	158	144	150

4. Depends on your results. Here is the line graph for the spare results.
5. Spare results:
   a) 20   b) 50   c) 70

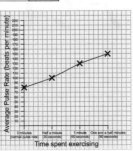

6. The longer the time spent exercising the higher the pulse rate.

---

7. Bob
8. tennis
   E.g. tennis works Liz's muscles more than playing catch, so her heart has to beat faster to get more blood to her muscles.
9. 100 seconds
10. longer, longer

Pages 23-24 — Drugs and Your Body

1. alcohol, nicotine, cannabis, heroin
2. cigarettes, cigars, headache tablets, wine
3. addicted, unwell, cocaine, chemical, nicotine
4.

	Drinking Alcohol (wine, beer, lager...)	Smoking Tobacco (cigarettes, cigars...)
Short-term effects (things that happen straight away)	Head feels funny	Head feels funny
	Slow reactions	Can't taste much
	Can't talk properly	Tar in lungs
Long-term effects (things that happen when you do it for years)	Heart disease	Heart disease
	Liver failure	Breathing problems
	Stomach ulcers	Lung cancer

5. Brain damage.

Page 25 — Drugs as Medicines

1. true, false, false, true, false
2. B, C

Mixed Questions — Pages 26-29

1. vitamins, fibre, minerals
2. C   3. heart, blood, blood vessels
4. Depends on your answer. Here are some ideas.
   Fish — tuna, sardines, cod, mackerel
   Vegetables — carrot, cauliflower, parsnip, sprouts
   Meat — chicken, beef, turkey, lamb, pork
   Fruit — banana, orange, strawberry, tangerine
   Fats — butter, chocolate, cheese
5. Drinking three bottles of cola each day. — Might have to have fillings. Eating ten chocolate bars a day. — Put on lots of weight. Drinking a glass of milk every day. — Grow strong bones. Eating a big bowl of rice in the morning. — Have loads of energy in the afternoon.
6. E.g. the walls of the heart are made of muscle.
   E.g. the blood vessels carry blood around the body.
   E.g. you can feel your pulse in your wrist.
7.

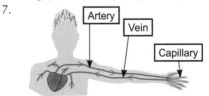

8. Flo's
   Flo, Max, Jim
9. E.g. water, nutrients, oxygen, carbon dioxide.
10. Alcohol — E.g. head feels funny, slow reactions, can't talk properly
    Tobacco — E.g. heart disease, breathing problems, lung cancer
    Solvents — e.g. brain
11. 3 is correct.
    E.g. Sentence 1 is wrong because you should always take medicine exactly as your doctor tells you to. / Sentence 2 is wrong because drugs in medicines are safe to use, as long as you follow the doctor's instructions.

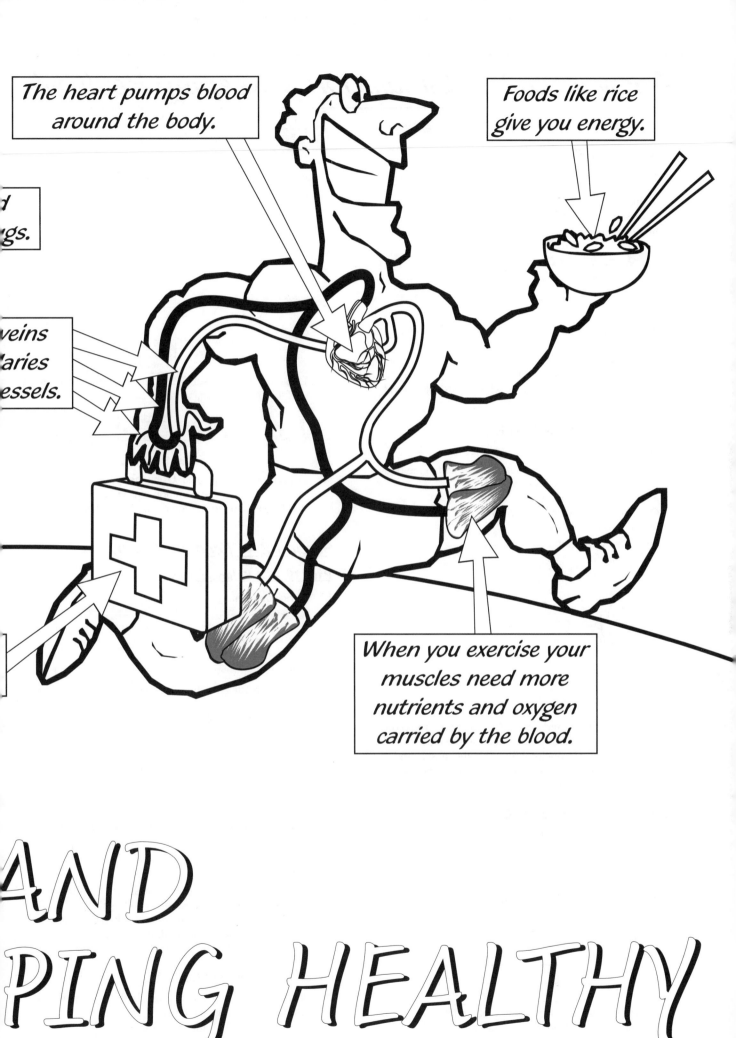

Answers to Y6 'Circulation & Keeping Healthy'

Section 1 — The Circulatory System

Page 1 — The Human Body

1. skeleton, muscles, digestive system
    1. skull
    2. spine / backbone
    3. hips / pelvis
    4. muscle
    5. oesophagus (food pipe)
    6. small intestine
2. blood, circulatory, organs, heart, vessels

Pages 2-3 — The Heart

1. The heart is inside the ribcage.
2. C
3. bones, protect
4. blood, pump, hot water, body, water/nutrients, water/
    nutrients
5. walls, muscle, contraction, squeeze
    The heart fills with blood. Then the muscles contract
    and the heart becomes smaller, which pushes the blood
    out and around the body.

Pages 4-5 — Blood and Blood Vessels

1. These should be ticked: capillary, artery, vein.
2. Arteries carry blood away from the heart and to the body.
    Blood is carried away from the body
    and back to the heart by veins.
    Capillaries allow substances to move
    in and out of the blood.
3. nutrients, water, carbon dioxide, oxygen
    carbon dioxide
    lungs
4. E.g.

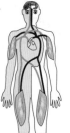

5. E.g. the heart beats and pushes the blood out. The blood
    travels through an artery until it reaches the muscle.
    The blood flows through capillaries in the muscle and
    enters veins when it leaves the muscle. The blood travels
    through the veins back to the heart.

Pages 6-9 — Calculating Pulse Rates

1. heart, beats, wrist, number, blood, pulse
2. A beat
    The number of times the heart beats in one minute.
3. Depends on your
    results. I've put
    in my results
    to give you an
    idea of what they
    should look like.

Beats in 30 seconds
37
38
40
39
37

4. Depends on your
    results.
5. You might have missed a beat, so you counted incorrectly.
    Your pulse rate may go up and down a little bit even if
    you're just sitting still.
6. Depends on your results. I've put in my results to give you

an idea of what they should look like.

Beats in 30 seconds	Pulse rate (beats per min)
37	74
38	76
39	78

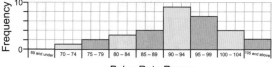

$74 + 76 + 78 = 228$
$228 \div 3 = 76$

7. Depends on your results.
    This table uses
    the spare results:

Average Pulse Rate	Tally	Frequency
69 and below		0
70 – 74	I	1
75 – 79	II	2
80 – 84	III	3
85 – 89	IIII	4
90 – 94	IIII IIII	9
95 – 99	IIII II	7
100 – 104	IIII	4
105 and above	II	2

8. Depends on your results. This chart uses the spare results:

    Frequency (y-axis), Pulse Rate Range (x-axis: 69 and under, 70 – 74, 75 – 79, 80 – 84, 85 – 89, 90 – 94, 95 – 99, 100 – 104, 105 and above)

9. Depends on your results. Using the spare results:
    90 – 94 was the most common pulse rate range, 95 – 99
    was the second most common and 69 and below was the
    least common.

Section 2 — Keeping Healthy

Page 10 — A Balanced Diet

1. Patrick and Lena
2.

Eating well should mean you will...	Eating badly could mean you will...
Grow well.	Get fat.
Be able to do lots of sports.	Have to have loads of fillings in your teeth.
Have loads of energy.	Get tired a lot.
Have strong bones and muscles.	Not feel so good.

    It doesn't matter which order the sentences are in.

Page 11 — Types of Food

1. sausages — meat   pear — fruit
    cabbage — vegetables   salmon — fish
    butter — fats   steak — meat
    carrots — vegetables   sardines — fish
    olive oil — fats   banana — fruit

Page 12 — Foods for Energy and Foods for Growth

1. Energy: rice, chips, spaghetti. Growth: beef, fish, milk.
2. 2 — The food gets broken down as it
        goes through her digestive system.
    3 — When it gets to the small intestine,
        the nutrients are absorbed into the blood.
    4 — The blood takes the nutrients back to the heart.
    5 — The heart beats and sends the blood
        with the nutrients to her muscles.

Page 13 — Sugar and Fat

1. crisps — fat   chocolate — both   jam — sugar
    lemonade — sugar   ice cream — both
    cheese — fat   fried egg & chips — fat
2. fat, teeth, fillings, vegetables, healthy

Testing an Idea

*About 250 years ago, sailors on long voyages would often get an illness called <u>scurvy</u>.
A doctor called James Lind thought that eating <u>citrus fruit</u> (lemons, limes or oranges) <u>might</u>
cure the illness. Read the write-up of the experiment he did and answer the questions.*

On the 20th May, 1747, I began my test with twelve patients who had scurvy on board a ship called "HMS Salisbury". Their cases were as similar as I could find. They all had rotting gums, spots, and weakness. They were all in the same cabin, and I gave them all the same food to eat for breakfast, lunch and dinner.

I gave two of the patients two pints of cider to drink each day. I gave two others weak sulphuric acid each day. I gave two others two spoonfuls of vinegar each day. I gave two half a pint of sea water to drink every day. I gave two others two oranges and one lemon each day. The last two patients were given a special mixture from the ship's surgeon, containing garlic, mustard seed and other things.

The result was that good effects were soon found from the use of oranges and lemons — one of the men who had taken them was fit for duty after just six days, and the other was also very well. The two men who took cider were only slightly better. None of the others were much better than at the beginning.*

1. Apart from their special treatments, James Lind gave each of the patients the same food to eat. Did that help to make it a **fair test**, or make it less fair? Explain your answer.

   ....

   ....

   ....

2. Write down **one** other thing James Lind did to help make the test **fair**.

   ....

   ....

3. Tick (✔) the **best** thing that James Lind could do to make sure that oranges and lemons really were a good cure, and that it wasn't just **chance**.

    Do a test with 12 other sick sailors, but this time instead of giving the sailors the same food to eat, give them different things to eat.

    Do a test with just one sick sailor, and give them all the special treatments at once.   Do the same test again with 12 other sick sailors.

*Adapted from James Lind's "A Treatise of Scurvy in Three Parts. Containing an inquiry into the Nature, Causes and Cure of that Disease, together with a Critical and Chronological View of what has been published on the subject".

INVESTIGATE •

Look in a book or on the Internet to find out what causes scurvy. Then write a letter to a friend to tell them about James Lind's experiment, the cure he found and why it worked.

Section 2 — Keeping Healthy

Exercise

When you <u>exercise</u>, your muscles work <u>harder</u>, you breathe <u>faster</u> and feel <u>hotter</u> — then you start to <u>feel tired</u>. After a short rest your body gets back to normal, but you might still be tired.

1. Circle all the people below who are doing things that will make them more **healthy**.

Marco

Carl

and 8...
... and 9...

Holly

Tony

Maddie

Boris

Diana

The Johnson Brothers

Theo

2. Circle the person out of each of these **pairs** whose muscles are working harder and who will feel **hotter** and **more tired** after the activity.

Remember — the <u>harder</u> you work and exercise, the <u>harder</u> your muscles work. And the <u>harder</u> your muscles work, the <u>hotter</u> and <u>more tired</u> you will feel.

Pierre

Yvette

Tomasz

– AAAA!!

Raj

Nelson

Frederick

Yvette and Pierre   Tomasz and Raj   Nelson and Frederick

Exercise

3. **Sit down** and relax for two minutes. Then count how many times you breathe out in **one minute**. Write the answer in here.

	Number of breaths taken per minute
When relaxed	
After exercise	
3 minutes after exercise	

4. **Run on the spot** as fast as you can for 30 seconds. Straight after you've done that, count the number of breaths you take in a minute. Write them in the second space in the table.

5. Sit still for **3 minutes** then count the number of breaths in a minute again and fill in the bottom space on the table.

6. Were you taking **more** breaths per minute when you were relaxed, or after you had done some exercise?

    ....

    ....

7. Did your breathing **return** to normal 3 minutes after exercise?

    ....

8. Fill in the gaps in these sentences with the correct word(s) from the **brackets**.

    Exercising is .... (**good** / **bad**) for you. It makes your

    muscles work .... (**harder** / **less hard**). This helps keep them

    healthy and .... (**weak** / **strong**). Sitting still and eating all

    the time is .... (**healthier** / **less healthy**) than exercising.

INVESTIGATE ·
*   *Do five different kinds of exercise — for example running, walking, skipping, star jumps*
    and sit ups. For each type of exercise, which muscles do you think you used the most?
    What was the most tiring exercise you did? Which exercise was the least tiring?

· ·

Exercise and Your Pulse

When you exercise, your muscles do more <u>work</u> than normal. Your <u>heart beats faster</u> to get blood (containing nutrients and oxygen) to your muscles faster, to give them more energy.

1.   Fill in the **missing words** in these sentences to explain what happens when you exercise. Use the words on the TV screen.

pulse   energy

exercise   beat

When you .... , your muscles work harder,

which means that they need more ....

Your heart has to .... faster, to get more oxygen and nutrients there.

You can tell how fast your heart is beating by checking your ....

2.   Look at what these people are doing, and then write down which parts of their bodies will need the **most energy**. Make sure you give a **reason** for each of your answers.

Martina is playing football.

Playing football mostly uses leg muscles.

So Martina's legs will need more energy when

she is playing football.

Chad is playing table tennis.

....

....

....

Yao is swimming.

....

....

....

Lori is running.

....

....

....

Exercise and Your Pulse

3. (Circle) the activity which will **increase** pulse rate the most.

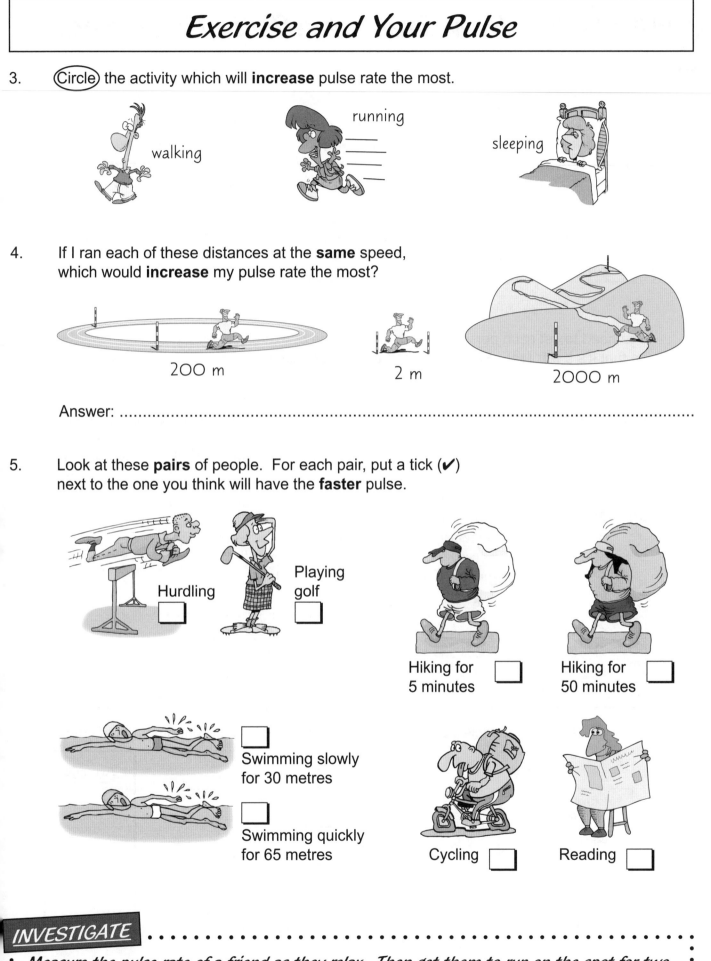

walking

running

sleeping

4. If I ran each of these distances at the **same** speed, which would **increase** my pulse rate the most?

200 m

2 m

2000 m

Answer: ....

5. Look at these **pairs** of people. For each pair, put a tick (✔) next to the one you think will have the **faster** pulse.

Hurdling ☐

Playing golf ☐

Hiking for 5 minutes ☐

Hiking for 50 minutes ☐

Swimming slowly for 30 metres ☐

Swimming quickly for 65 metres ☐

Cycling ☐

Reading ☐

INVESTIGATE ·

Measure the pulse rate of a friend as they relax. Then get them to run on the spot for two minutes. Measure their pulse rate again afterwards, and explain to them why it is higher.

MINI-PROJECT
How Exercise Affects Pulse Rate

This project is to find out how the length of time you exercise affects the increase in your pulse rate. The easiest way to do this is to measure your pulse before you do any exercise and after you do various amounts of exercise.

1. You need to try it out on a few people, to make sure your results are **reliable**.
    Tick (✔) **one** box to show how many people you think you should do the experiment on.

    ☐ 1 person   ☐ 4 - 10 people   ☐ 6 million people   ☐ 500 people

2. You need to get each person to do the same type of exercise, so that it's a **fair test**. Pick any **one** of these, and circle it: jogging on the spot   star jumps   skipping

3. Use the **method** below to do the experiment and fill in the **table** at the bottom of the page.

> ○ Equipment: A stopwatch, or a clock with a seconds hand.
> ○ Method:
> ○   1) Write your name in the top row of the table.
> ○   2) Measure normal pulse rate (number of beats per minute when you've been resting) and write it in the table, under your name.
> ○   3) Do the exercise you chose in question 2, for 30 seconds (half a minute), then measure your pulse rate and write it in the table.
> ○   4) Wait for your pulse rate to go back to normal.
> ○   5) Do the same exercise for 1 minute, then measure your pulse rate, and write it in the table.
> ○   6) Wait for your pulse rate to go back to normal.
> ○   7) Do the exercise for 1 and a half minutes, then measure your pulse rate, and write it in the table.
> ○   8) Test three other people (remembering to put their names at the top), then work out all the average pulse rates.

Don't worry if you can't do this experiment — there are some spare results at the bottom of this page for you to use instead.

See page 7 for how to measure your pulse rate.

Table of 4 people's pulse rates after exercising for different amounts of time

Name:					Average
Normal pulse rate (beats per minute)					
Pulse rate after half a minute of exercise					
Pulse rate after 1 minute of exercise					
Pulse rate after 1 and a half minutes of exercise					

Spare results: Normal — Me 72, Ed 80, Liz 78, Jo 90. After half a minute of exercise — Me 94, Ed 99, Liz 97, Jo 110. After one minute of exercise — Me 135, Ed 125, Liz 133, Jo 127. After one and a half minutes of exercise — Me 152, Ed 146, Liz 158, Jo 144

How Exercise Affects Pulse Rate

MINI-PROJECT

4. Draw a **line graph** of the average pulse rates from the last page.
To draw the line graph, mark a **cross** to show the average pulse rate after
each amount of exercise. Then draw **straight lines** to join up the crosses.

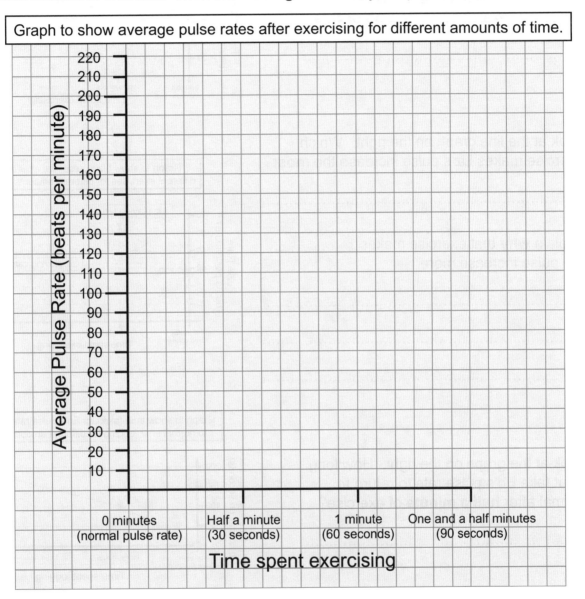

Graph to show average pulse rates after exercising for different amounts of time.

Average Pulse Rate (beats per minute)

220
210
200
190
180
170
160
150
140
130
120
110
100
90
80
70
60
50
40
30
20
10

| 0 minutes (normal pulse rate) | Half a minute (30 seconds) | 1 minute (60 seconds) | One and a half minutes (90 seconds) |

Time spent exercising

5. How many beats per minute did the average pulse rate **go up** from the
normal pulse rate after the following amounts of time spent exercising?

a) Half a minute: ....

b) One minute: ....

c) One and a half minutes: ....

6. What is the **relationship** between the length of time spent exercising
and the increase in pulse rate? Finish the sentence below.

The longer the time spent exercising ....

How Exercise Affects Pulse Rate

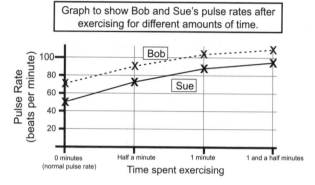

Graph to show Bob and Sue's pulse rates after exercising for different amounts of time.

7.   Look at this line graph. Whose pulse rate was **faster** after the one and a half minutes of exercise? Write **Bob** or **Sue**.

....

8.   Look at the line graph on the right. Which exercise makes Liz's pulse increase the **most**?

....

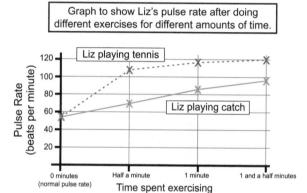

Graph to show Liz's pulse rate after doing different exercises for different amounts of time.

Explain **why** that exercise makes her pulse increase more.

....

....

....

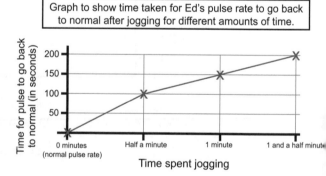

Graph to show time taken for Ed's pulse rate to go back to normal after jogging for different amounts of time.

9.   Look at the graph on the right. How long did it take Ed's pulse rate to return to normal after **half a minute** of exercise?

....

10.   What is the **relationship** between the length of time spent exercising and the length of time taken for the pulse to go back to normal? Fill in the blanks.

The .... you exercise, the ....

it takes for your pulse to go back to normal.

EXTRA PROJECT

Do the experiment again using a different type of exercise.
Draw your results on the same graph as the first experiment, and use it to compare the two.
Which exercise gave you higher average pulse rates? Is that what you expected?

Drugs and Your Body

A <u>drug</u> is anything you take that changes how your body <u>works</u>
— like making your blood pressure higher, or changing the way your brain works.

1. Which of the things below are **drugs**? Tick (✔) the right ones.

   ☐ alcohol ☐ vitamins ☐ soap ☐ cannabis

   ☐ cabbage ☐ nicotine ☐ petrol ☐ heroin

2. Ring the **four** things below that have drugs in them.

   Cigarettes

   Sweets

   Computer games

   Wine

   Headache tablets

   Bread

   Cigars

3. Use the words in the **box** to fill in the gaps in the sentences.

chemical	nicotine	cocaine	addicted	unwell

   People can get .... to drugs.

   When you are addicted to a drug, you can feel .... if you stop taking it.

   Drugs like .... and heroin are both very addictive. People get addicted to

   smoking because tobacco contains a .... called ....

Drugs and Your Body

4. In the boxes are some of the things that can happen when you drink **alcohol** or **smoke**. Complete the **table** below to show which effect goes with which drug.

Short-term effects
Slow reactions
Can't talk properly
Tar in lungs

Long-term effects
Liver failure
Lung cancer
Stomach ulcers

Some things, like
<u>heart disease</u>, can be
caused by <u>either</u>
drinking or smoking.

	Drinking Alcohol (wine, beer, lager...)	Smoking Tobacco (cigarettes, cigars...)
Short-term effects (things that happen straight away)	Head feels funny	Head feels funny
		Can't taste much
Long-term effects (things that happen when you do it for years)	Heart disease	Heart disease
		Breathing problems

5. **Solvents**, like glue, can be used as drugs.
   Tick (✔) one box below that is a **long-term effect** of solvent abuse.

   ☐ Can't talk properly   ☐ Headache   ☐ Feeling sleepy

   ☐ Feeling very ill   ☐ Brain damage

INVESTIGATE ....

- *Research the dangers of smoking on the Internet or in a book. Then make a leaflet saying*
- *what the dangers are and explaining them. You should mention the short-term effects*
- *and the long-term effects, as well as which organs could be harmed.*

Drugs as Medicines

Doctors can give you medicines to make you better when you're <u>ill</u>.
But medicines are drugs and they can be <u>dangerous</u> if you don't use them properly.

1. Here are some sentences about medicines. Tick (✔) **true** or **false** for each sentence.

	TRUE	FALSE
Some drugs are medicines that can help ill people to get better.	☐	☐
Medicine always tastes of strawberry.	☐	☐
Doctors give patients medicine to make them feel worse.	☐	☐
When the doctor gives you medicine, you should always use it the way the doctor tells you to.	☐	☐
Medicines can't do you any harm.	☐	☐

2. Why might a doctor give a patient some medicine to get rid of bad headaches, that also makes them sleepy? Pick out **two** good reasons and write the **letters** underneath.

Ⓐ If they go to sleep, they might forget they've got a headache.

Ⓑ It's more important to get rid of the headaches, because the patient is in pain.

Most medicines are fairly safe, but some can have side-effects — they might cure one thing, but also make you feel sleepy, or a bit sick.

Ⓒ Feeling sleepy will wear off when they finish the medicine.

Ⓓ Doctors don't care what happens to people.

Two good reasons are: .... and ....

INVESTIGATE . . . .

Ask an adult to show you some different medicines. See if you can write down something
that each one treats, what one of the side-effects is, and the name of the drug it contains.

Mixed Questions

You probably think you know all there is to know about circulation and keeping healthy now.
So here are four pages of questions for you to get your teeth into...

1.   Circle the things that you get loads of in **fruit** and **vegetables**.

fat   vitamins   concrete   minerals   fibre   meat

2.   Tick (✔) the body where the **heart** is in the **right place**.

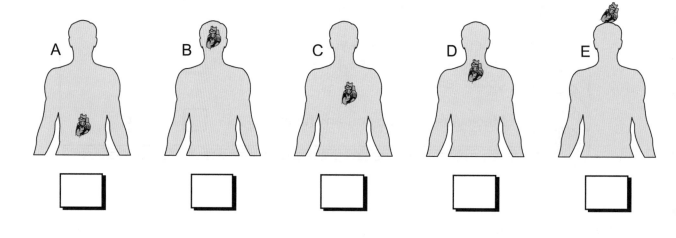

3.   Circle the **three** parts of the circulatory system shown below.

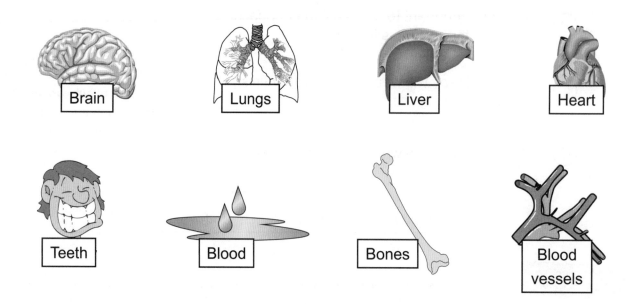

Mixed Questions

4. Here are **five** different groups of food.
    For each one, write down **three foods** that belong in that group.

Fish
....
....
....

Vegetables
....
....
....

Meat
....
....
....

Fruit
....
....
....

Fats
....
....
....

5. Draw **arrows** to match up each **activity** with a possible **outcome**.
    One has been done for you. Use each outcome only once.

Activity

Eating vegetables every day.

Drinking three bottles of cola each day.

Eating ten chocolate bars a day.

Drinking a glass of milk every day.

Eating a big bowl of rice in the morning.

Outcome

Put on lots of weight.

Have loads of energy in the afternoon.

Grow strong bones.

Be full of vitamins.

Might have to have fillings.

Mixed Questions

6. Each of these sentences contains **one** mistake. **Rewrite** each sentence so that it is correct.

    The walls of the heart are made of veins.

    ....

    The bones carry blood around the body.

    ....

    You can't feel your pulse in your wrist.

    ....

7. This picture shows some of the **blood vessels** in Edward's arm.
    Fill in the **labels** with the correct name for each blood vessel.

    HINT: Look at the direction of the arrows on the blood vessels to help you.

    ....

    ....

    ....

8. Look at the **pictures** and then answer the questions below.

    Max

    Jim

    Flo

    Whose muscles are working **hardest**?

    ....

    Put the three people in order of pulse rate from **fastest** to **slowest**.

    Fastest: .... Middle: .... Slowest: ....

Mixed Questions

9. What does the **blood transport** around the body?

    ....

    ....

10. Write down **two** short-term effects of drinking **alcohol**.

    1. ....

    2. ....

    Write down **two** long-term effects of smoking **tobacco**.

    1. ....

    2. ....

    Write down **one** organ of the body that could be damaged by **solvents**.

    ....

11. A **doctor** has given Nadia a bottle of **medicine** to cure her ear infection.
    The doctor told Nadia to take **two spoonfuls** each day for a week. What should Nadia do?
    Tick (✔) the box next to the sentence that's **correct**.

    | 1. She should drink the whole bottle at once so that she gets better sooner. | ☐ |

    | 2. She shouldn't take the medicine because all drugs are harmful. | ☐ |

    | 3. She should take the medicine exactly as the doctor told her to. | ☐ |

    Now pick one of the sentences that you **didn't** tick and explain why it is **wrong**.

    Sentence .... is wrong because ....

    ....

    ....

Glossary

Alcohol	A **drug** that's found in some drinks like wine and beer. If you drink too much it can damage your **heart**, **liver** and **stomach**.
Artery	A **blood vessel** which carries blood **away** from the heart.
Blood	The **red liquid** that's pumped around the body by the **heart**. It **transports** nutrients, water and oxygen, as well as waste products.
Capillary	A **blood vessel** that lets things move **in** and **out** of the blood.
Drug	Something you take that **changes** how your **body works**.
Heart	The organ that **pumps** blood around the body.
Medicine	A useful **drug** that helps make you **better** when you're **ill**.
Minerals	Substances found in **fruit** and **vegetables** that keep you healthy. They're also found in other foods like meat, fish, milk and nuts.
Nicotine	A **chemical** in cigarettes that is **addictive**, so people who smoke find it **hard to stop** even if they want to.
Pulse	The movement of **blood** through blood vessels that you can feel in your **wrist** and **neck**. Your **pulse rate** is **higher** when you're **exercising**.
Scurvy	An **illness** caused by not having enough **vitamin C**.
Tobacco	A substance that causes **heart disease**, **lung cancer** and **breathing problems**. Cigarettes and cigars contain tobacco.
Vein	A **blood vessel** that takes blood **back** to the heart.
Vitamins	Substances found in **fruit** and **vegetables** that keep you healthy. They're also found in other foods like fish, milk and fats.

S6A22